Stay Safe with Thomas

✔ KU-540-003

Based on
The Railway Series
by the
Rev. W. Awdry

First published in Great Britain 2018 by Dean,
an imprint of Egmont Books UK Limited
2 Minster Court, 10th Floor, London EC3R 7BB

Thomas the Tank Engine & Friends™

CREATED BY BRITT ALLCROFT

Illustrated by Robin Davies. Written by Jane Riordan.
Designed by Martin Aggett

ISBN: 978 0 6035 7593 8
70212/004

Printed in Great Britain

Egmont takes its responsibility to the planet and its inhabitants
very seriously. We aim to use papers from well-managed forests
run by responsible suppliers.

Stay safe online. Egmont is not responsible
for content hosted by third parties.

Thomas the Tank Engine had six small wheels, a short stumpy funnel, a short stumpy boiler and a short stumpy dome.

Thomas was a cheeky, little engine. He thought he knew everything there was to know about The Fat Controller's railway.

One morning, The Fat Controller came to the Sheds to give Thomas his jobs for the day.

"Thomas, it is your job to keep yourself and all your passengers safe," warned The Fat Controller. "You must never be silly when you're out on the tracks."

But Thomas didn't listen. He was in a silly, cheeky mood. He rushed to the Water Tower to fill up his boiler before he started his day.

"Having fun is more important than being safe," he giggled, as he let out a huge burst of steam!

Once Thomas was clean, his coaches, Annie and Clarabel, were coupled up to him and off they went.

Thomas saw his friend Bertie driving along the road ahead of him.

"I can't be slower than a bus," he thought.

Thomas sped up and raced Bertie through the countryside.

A little further along, the road turned and crossed the track.

"Why are you waiting there?" teased Thomas, as he whooshed past Bertie at the level crossing. "Don't you want to race?"

But Thomas didn't stop to hear Bertie's reply, he sped on past a farm.

"There are animals close to the track, Thomas," warned Annie. "Don't go too fast."

But Thomas didn't listen, he raced the horse.

Thomas was going faster than ever before.

He was going so fast that he couldn't stop at the next station – he just whooshed through.

"Slow down!" called the Station Workers.

When Thomas eventually managed to stop, The Fat Controller was cross.

"What you did today was very dangerous, Thomas," said The Fat Controller. "It was wrong to encourage Bertie to race. Anyone using the road must stop if the level crossing gates are closed or if there is a red light."

Then The Fat Controller reminded Thomas about the time a gate had been left open. A herd of cows had wandered onto the tracks and it had nearly caused a nasty accident.

"People must always close gates behind them," said The Fat Controller, "and engines must watch out for animals."

"When you're at a station," continued The Fat Controller, "you must watch out for children standing too close to the tracks and for people who might have dropped something on the tracks."

"Always tell children to stand back, Thomas," he continued, "and if anyone has dropped something on the track they must talk to someone who works at the station and never try to get it themselves."

"Keeping everyone safe is a big, important job," replied Thomas.

"It is," said The Fat Controller. "But I'm here to help and so are the engineers on the railway. They work in all weathers to keep the tracks clear and safe for the engines and the passengers."

As the stars came out and Thomas made his way back to the Engine Sheds, he knew that being safe, and reminding passengers to keep safe, was the most important thing of all.

"Peep! Peep!" he tooted to the engineers, working through the night to keep the railway running safely.

When you next go on a train journey, tick the boxes to show that you know how to stay safe.

I didn't throw anything onto the tracks ☐

I waited at a level crossing and did what the sign said ☐

I stood back from the platform edge ☐

I didn't stop on the tracks at the level crossing ☐

I looked in both directions at the level crossing ☐

I stayed with my grown-up at the station ☐

I didn't pick anything up from the tracks ☐

I didn't play on the train tracks ☐

I walked carefully on the platform ☐